The DIAMOND EGG of WONDERS

To NOAM,

ENJOY THE ADVENTURE!

ALL THE BEST

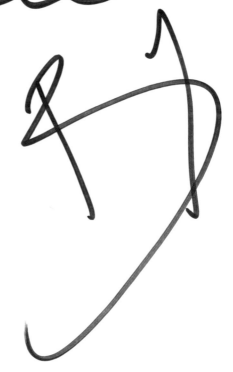

This book is dedicated to the following, without whom none of this would be possible:
Our parents, who have always supported and encouraged us to chase our dreams.
Mimi and Esther, for motivating us every day to transform those dreams into reality.
All our readers, whose enthusiasm inspires us to continue dreaming.

The Etherington Brothers
- Adventures in Words and Pictures -
www.theetheringtonbrothers.blogspot.com

MONKEY NUTS: THE DIAMOND EGG OF WONDERS

A DAVID FICKLING BOOK 978 0 385 61906 6

First published thanks to the amazing DFC weekly comic,
May 2008 – March 2009 (Come back soon!!)

This edition published in Great Britain in 2010 by David Fickling Books,
a division of Random House Children's Books
A Random House Group Company

3 5 7 9 10 8 6 4

DAVID FICKLING BOOKS
31 Beaumont Street, Oxford, OX1 2NP

www.kidsatrandomhouse.co.uk

Addresses for companies within The Random House Group Limited can be found at:
www.randomhouse.co.uk/offices.htm

THE RANDOM HOUSE GROUP Limited Reg. No. 954009

A CIP catalogue record for this book is available from the British Library.

Printed and bound in China

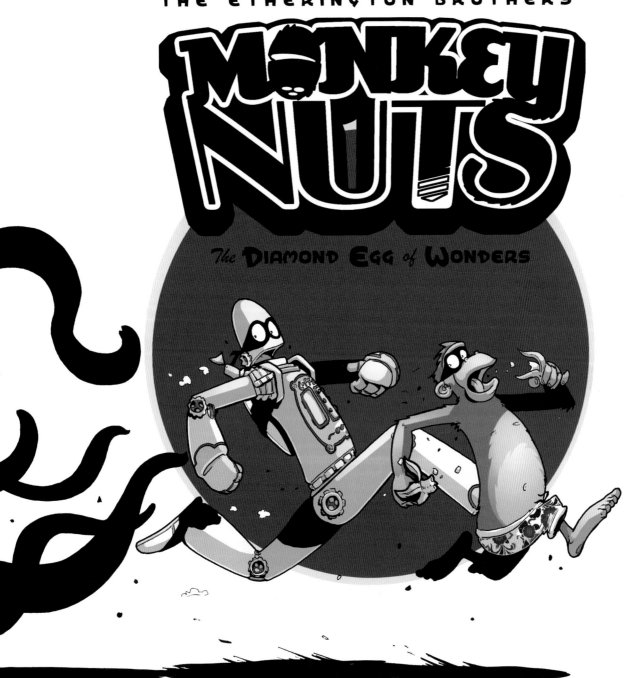

THE ETHERINGTON BROTHERS

MONKEY NUTS

The DIAMOND EGG of WONDERS

David Fickling Books

OXFORD · NEW YORK

INSIDE

I, **LORD TERRA**, HAVE DISCOVERED THE LOCATION OF THE **DIAMOND EGG OF WONDERS**! IT IS A PRICELESS, MYSTICAL TREASURE WITH UNLIMITED POWER!

ERM, **ERIC?**...

GOOBER AN' ME WANTS TO KNOW IF WE CAN EATS DA DIAMOND EGG WHEN WE GETS IT.

YEAH ... AN' DOES IT TASTE LIKE A NORMAL EGG?

BURPLE, STOP CALLING ME **ERIC**! I'VE TOLD YOU A HUNDRED TIMES, I'M **LORD TERRA** NOW! ERIC IS A RUBBISH NAME FOR AN EVIL MASTERMIND!

AND NO, YOU CANNOT EAT THE EGG! IT IS WORTH MORE THAN THIS FORTRESS. NOW, PAY ATTENTION, HENCHMEN. **THIS** IS A MAP.

WHACK

AND **THIS** IS THE ISLA DE MONSTERA. THE EGG IS HIDDEN SOMEWHERE ON THIS PARADISE!

SO WHY IS WE SITTIN' HERE? LET'S FIRE UP TABITHA AND GO GETS IT!

GOOD ONE, BURPLE! NOW YOU IS FINKIN'!

NO. YOU ARE NOT.

BONK

DO YOU REMEMBER ON TUESDAY WHEN WE STOPPED OFF FOR LUNCH AT THAT LITTLE ISLAND WHERE THE NATIVES WORSHIPPED A **FOOTBALL?**

UM, YEAH.

ONE OF THE VILLAGERS I **ATE** MUST HAVE PASSED HIS SELL-BY DATE. I HAD A HORRIBLE BOUT OF FOOD POISONING WHICH BROUGHT ON -- **THE VISION!**

I SAW TWO CREATURES, TWO WARRIORS OF GOOD, WHO HAVE THE POWER TO FOIL MY SCHEME! I DID A LITTLE DRAWING OF THEM...

EARLIER TODAY I ACTIVATED TABITHA'S SONIC **'MONSTER MAGNET'**. SOON EVERY LOONY AND WEIRDO IN THE AREA WILL BE DRAWN TO THIS ISLAND WITH THE SAME GOAL: TO CAUSE LOTS OF TROUBLE AND **DESTROY** THESE CHUMPS!

THE DIAMOND EGG OF WONDERS SHALL BE MINE! MWAHAHAHA!

AND SO LORD TERRA SENT HIS TERRIBLE SIGNAL PULSING UPWARDS THROUGH THE EARTH. HE REALLY IS VERY NAUGHTY.

CHAPTER TWO
WHEN ROBOT MEETS MONKEY!

MEANWHILE IN CHUMP TOWN - A MYSTERIOUS CITY ON THE REALLY MYSTERIOUS ISLA DE MONSTERA, BASED SMACK IN THE MIDDLE OF THE REALLY, REALLY MYSTERIOUS BERMUDA TRIANGLE (AND DIRECTLY ABOVE LORD TERRA'S MONSTER MAGNET) - THE DAY WAS STARTING PEACEFULLY...

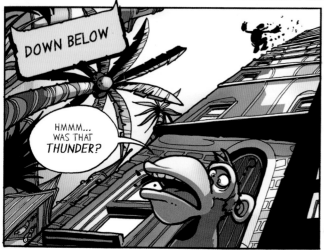

8

10

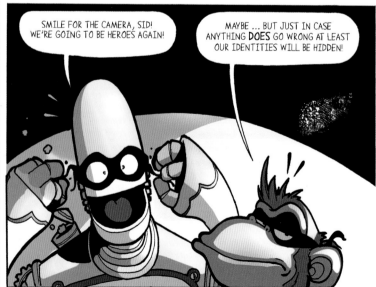

15

WITHIN MOMENTS THE POOR CONFUSED RESIDENTS OF CHUMP TOWN WERE ONCE MORE FLEEING FOR THEIR HAPLESS LIVES...

GRROOOOOAR!

DRIIIING
DRIIIING

PEOPLE ARE GOING TO SAY THIS IS **MY** FAULT, AREN'T THEY?

NO! EVERYONE LOVES YOU, SID! WELL ... ALMOST EVERYONE.

DOWN WITH SID!

HANG THE MONKEY!

BOO! HISS!

GO, RIVET GO!

THANK GOODNESS I'M WEARING MY MASK! C'MON, RIVET, LET'S COOL THIS FIERY FIEND DOWN A LITTLE!

16

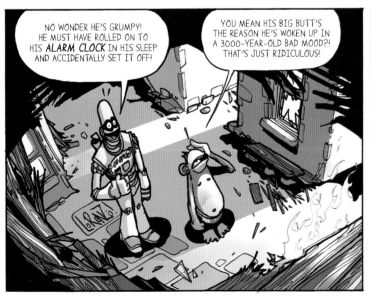

17

A WEEK PASSES UNEVENTFULLY AND THE MONKEY NUTS CREW DECIDE TO TAKE A WELL-DESERVED BREAK. BUT BENEATH THE STILL COASTAL WATERS DARK FORCES ARE DRAWN CLOSER UNDER LORD TERRA'S HYPNOTIC SPELL...

BEEEP BEEEP BEEEP BEEEP BEEEP

WELL BOYS, THIS IS THE LIFE!

IT CERTAINLY IS A NICE CHANGE OF PACE! NO ONE'S GOING TO TRY AND KILL US HERE!

HMMM ... I'M NOT SO SURE ABOUT THAT, RIVET.

SOMETHING PECULIAR IS GOING ON. TWO ATTACKS ON THE TOWN IN A WEEK IS **ONE** ATTACK TOO MANY!

NAH, THESE THINGS JUST HAPPEN, TUFT!

ARE YOU SURE ABOUT THAT, SID? IF THE CHIEF'S WORRIED, THEN I'M WORRIED!

WILL YOU BOTH RELAX! WE'RE ON HOLIDAY, AND WE'RE PERFECTLY SAFE! **NOTHING** CAN GO WRONG...

ABANDON HOPE ALL YE WHO FISH THESE WATERS!

W EAR BEE MONSTAS

CHAPTER FOUR
go FiSH!

WOAH! I THINK I'VE GOT A BITE!

SWEET BANANAS! <NGGGGGN!> IT'S A BIG ONE!

REALLY? HOW CAN YOU TELL? I CAN'T SEE A THING.

I CAN TELL, RIVET, YOU SILLY BAG OF BOLTS, BECAUSE IT'S ABOUT TO PULL ME OVERBOARD!

GRAB HOLD BOYS!

IF I'D KNOWN IT WAS GOING TO BE THIS MUCH HARD WORK I'D HAVE BROUGHT MY BIGGER ARMS!

IT'S PULLING THE BOAT! WOW! THIS FISH MUST BE A MONSTER!

HAHA ... UM, TUFT? I THINK IT'S OKAY FOR YOU TO LET GO!

LET GO? OKAY. IF YOU SAY SO.

NOT YOOOOOOU—

YANK

SPLOOOOOOSH

CHIEF? DOES THAT NORMALLY HAPPEN?

SOMETIMES. I KNEW I SHOULD HAVE HELD ON!

VLOOOOOSH

SID! THERE YOU ARE!

SO THEN CHAMP, DID YOU CATCH THAT TRICKY FISH?

ER ... NOT EXACTLY! I THINK THERE'S SOMETHING YOU SHOULD BOTH KNOW...

EXCUSE ME, GENTLEMEN. THIS IS A PRIVATE AREA. I'M AFRAID YOU'RE TRESPASSING.

21

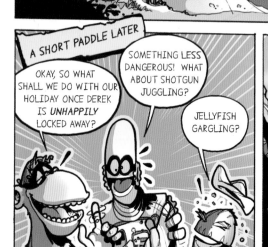

24

RETURNING FROM THEIR WELL-EARNED HOLIDAY, SID AND RIVET HEAD INTO CHUMP TOWN FOR AN IMPORTANT ERRAND. ALL APPEARS TO BE QUIET, BUT UNBEKNOWNST TO OUR HEROES, THE MONSTER MAGNET'S JUNGLE DRUMBEAT OF EVIL, ER, BEATS ON!

NOW LISTEN UP, *FEATHERS*, I REALLY DON'T SEE WHAT THE PROBLEM IS!

SHALL I EXPLAIN HOW THIS WORKS *AGAIN*, SIR?

THIS IS A **BANK**, SIR. FOLKS COME IN, OPEN ACCOUNTS AND DEPOSIT THEIR SAVINGS, SIR.

BUT THAT'S WHAT I'M *TRYING* TO DO!

THIS, SIR, IS A *BANANA*.

WELL SPOTTED! I'VE GOT *LOTS* MORE AND I'D LIKE YOU TO LOOK AFTER THEM UNTIL I'M *HUNGRY*!

WOULD YOU LIKE ME TO CALL YOU A DOCTOR, SIR? YOU SOUND LIKE A CRAZY PERSON.

3RD NATIONAL BANANA BANK OF CHUMP TOWN

CHAPTER FIVE
THE BANK RUSTLE HUSTLE!

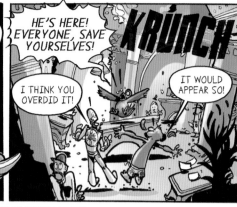

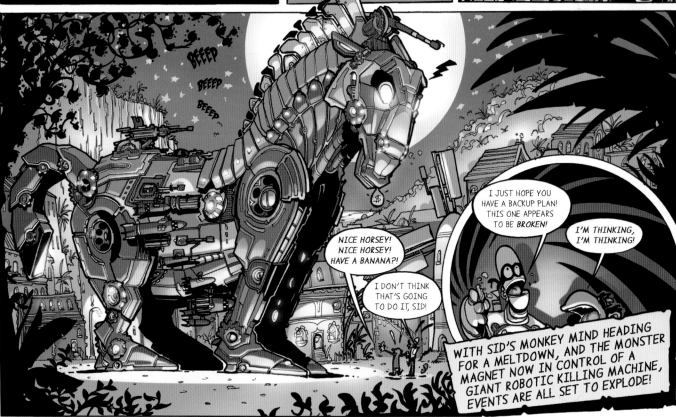

27

INSIDE HORSEY

THAT CHEEKY MONKEY! ACTIVATING TARGETING SYSTEMS!...

CLICK

CHUNK

THUNK

BANG BOOM GOOM

I HOPE YOU'RE NEARLY READY, BOYS! I'M RUNNING OUT OF AMMO!

SID! THAT WAS MY COUSIN, JEFF, YOU JUST THREW! HOW'S THE SCULPTING GOING, RIVET? YOU BETTER FINISH BEFORE THAT SILLY CHUMP USES ANOTHER MEMBER OF MY FAMILY AS A WEAPON!

WELL, I'M NOT VERY HAPPY WITH THE EARS BUT I GUESS SHE'LL HAVE TO DO!

WHA--?!

HEY THERE NEIGHHHHBOUR! HOW'S IT GOING?

DROP

HORSEY! WHY HAVE YE DROPPED THE BOOTY? WHY CAN'T I CONTROL YE!

OVERRIDE USER! EJECT BOSSY BLACK BEARD!

NO, HORSEY! YOU CAN'T GET RID OF ME!

BYE!

HORSEY! NO!

GOTCHA! LOOKS LIKE ALL'S FAIR IN LOVE AND WAR! HEHEHEHE!

WHOOMPH

$

WELL, BOYS, YOU'VE CAUGHT THE THIEF, CALMED THE GIANT HORSE ROBOT AND MADE THE BANKS SAFE AGAIN!

TRUE, BUT I'LL BE KEEPING MY BANANAS IN THE SAFEST PLACE OF ALL: MY BELLY!

THE BANK RUSTLING THREAT HAD BEEN VANQUISHED, BUT VICTORY LOOKED TO BE SHORT-LIVED FOR THE MONKEY NUTS TEAM. THEY NEEDED TO GET TO THE BOTTOM OF THIS CRIMEWAVE MYSTERY... ...AND FAST!

$

BUT **WHAT** IS A 'MUCKYBUTT'? AND **WHY** IS THE TEMPLE SHAKING? WHAT'S GOING **ON?!**

TROUBLE, THAT'S WHAT. OOOH, MUCKYBUTT SEEMS TO BE IN AN AWFUL MOOD! I DON'T KNOW WHAT'S GOT INTO HIM...

C'MON, RIVET, LET'S TAKE A PEEK OUTSIDE!

STRANGE ... EVERYTHING SEEMS FINE!

UM, YOU MIGHT WANT TO GET **ANOTHER** SECOND OPINION! LOOK **BELOW** YOU, SID!

AH ... YEP ... OKAY! NOT GOOD!

MY THOUGHTS EXACTLY!

ARE WE ON A SPECIAL SIGHT-SEEING TOUR? IS **THAT** WHY TUFT SENT US HERE?

I'D LIKE TO SAY YES ... BUT I'M GOING TO SAY NO! POTTYBOT?! WHAT IS HAPPENING?

THAT'S 'EMPEROR' POTTYBOT TO YOU. I MAY BE A FLOATING VOICE BUT I STILL DEMAND A LITTLE **RESPECT**.

THE MUCKYBUTT TEMPLE IS MY **GUARDIAN**. BY REFUSING TO LEAVE A GOLD OFFERING - AND FOR BEING A MONKEY - YOU APPEAR TO HAVE ANNOYED HIM GREATLY.

AS YOU ARE TRAPPED IN HERE, HE WILL DESTROY THE FIRST THING HE SEES: **CHUMP TOWN!** ... JUST LIKE HE ALWAYS DOES.

UM ... THIS ONE REALLY **IS** MY FAULT, ISN'T IT?

CERTAINLY LOOKS THAT WAY, SID! HOW ARE WE GOING TO SAVE THE DAY **THIS** TIME?!

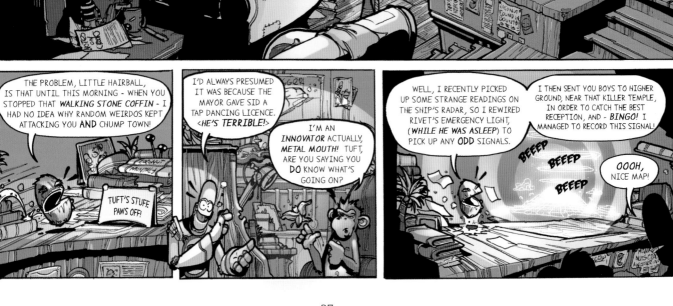

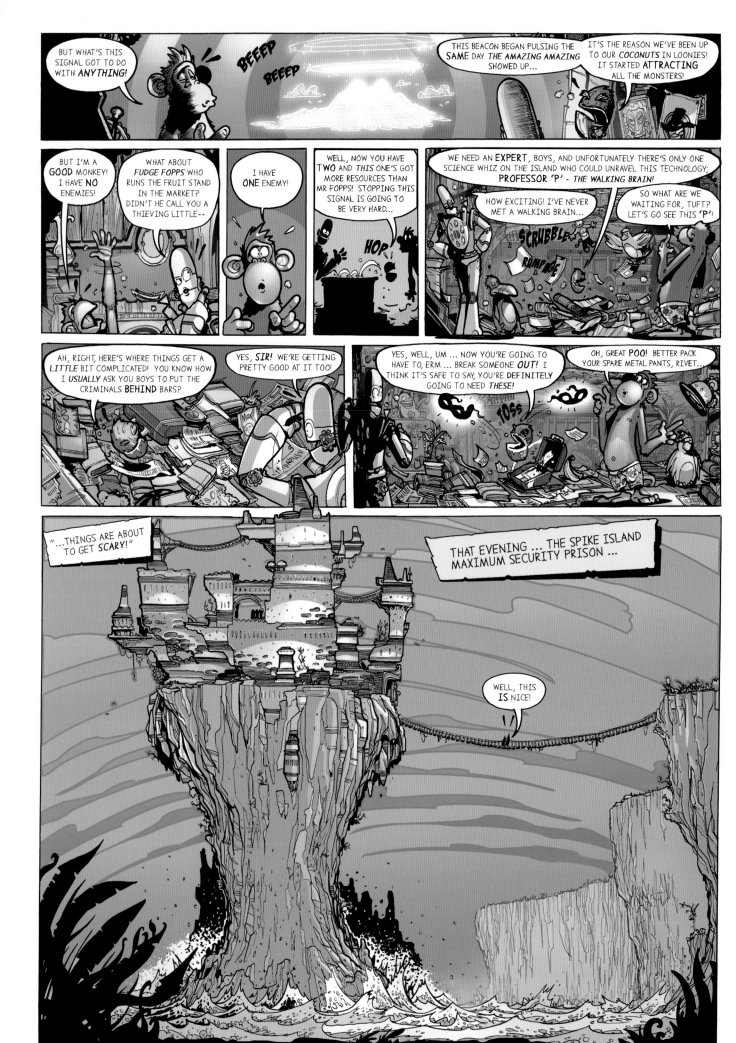

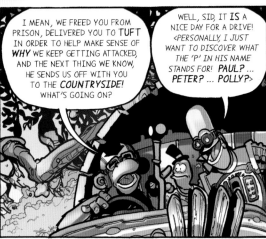

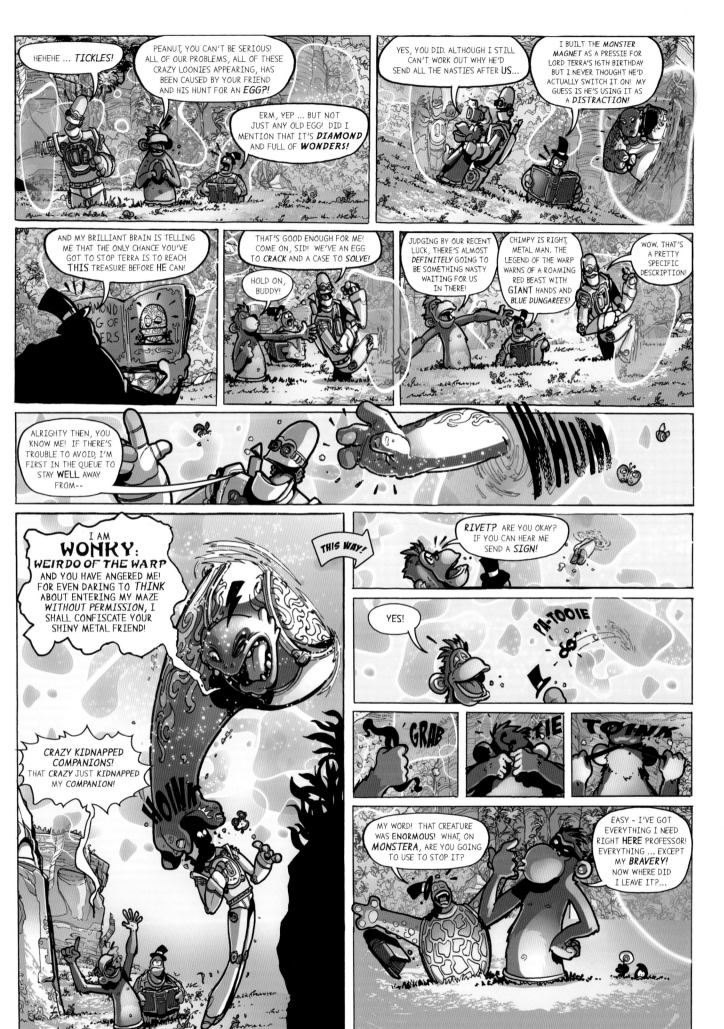

AND IT'S TIME TO *POKE* SOMETHING! LET'S SEE WHAT'S THROUGH WARP HOLE NUMBER *ONE*...

WOW! *SPORTY SHORTS*, MISTER! WHERE DID YOU GET THEM FROM?

THEY'RE *YOURS*, YOU SILLY CHUMP! YOU'RE HAVING A CHAT WITH YOUR OWN *BOTTOM!*

OOF! WELL DON'T *I* FEEL SILLY?!

BOOT

CAN YOU FOOLS HELP ME? I'M TRYING TO SAVE MY PENNIES IN THIS 'MONEY BOX' ONLY I CANNOT SEEM TO FIND THE SLOT! HARDY~HAR~HAR!

SID! SAVE YOURSELF! I'M RECYCLABLE!

NO ONE USES MY PAL AS A *PIGGY BANK!* HERE I COME--

WHUM

HOP   SKIP

OH DEAR. THAT'S *EXACTLY* WHAT I TRIED ON MY FIRST ATTEMPT! SAME RESULT TOO. STILL GOT THE SCAR TO SHOW FOR IT.

YOW!

WHAM

...GAAAAH...

HMMM ... IF ONLY THERE WAS SOME WAY TO *MARK* A ROUTE THROUGH THE MAZE...

WHAT, LIKE A TRAIL OF *BREADCRUMBS* OR...

HA! I'VE GOT IT! TUFT WAS RIGHT ABOUT YOU, P - YOU ARE A *GENIUS!*

LOOSE THREAD!

POINK

THIS LOOSE THREAD FROM MY SHORTS WILL CREATE THE *PERFECT* TRAIL ... AND PERHAPS A *SURPRISE* FOR OLD WONKY!

WHAT A CUNNING CHIMP!

TIE

HOLD TIGHT, RIVET! I'M TAKING A *STROLL*, THROUGH A *HOLE*, TO CATCH A *TROLL!*

WHUM

WHUM

UNRAVEL

WHUM

UNRAVEL

POINK

48

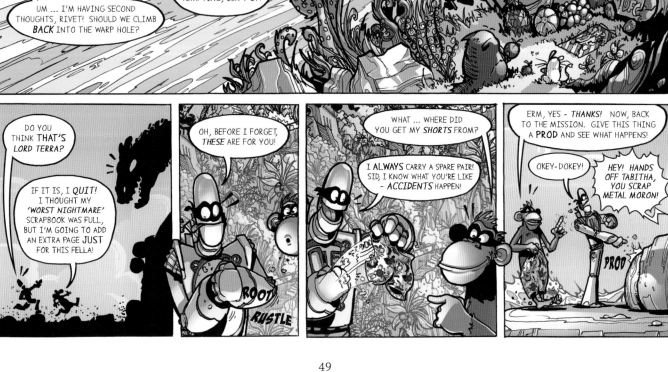

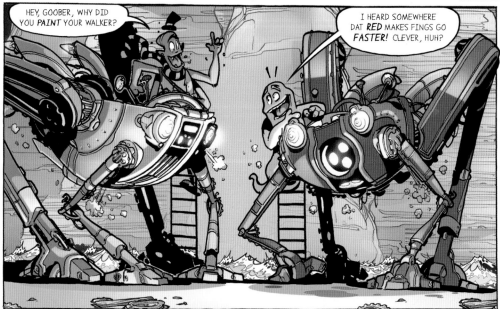

52

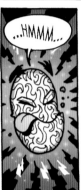
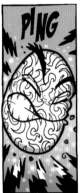

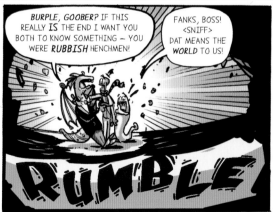

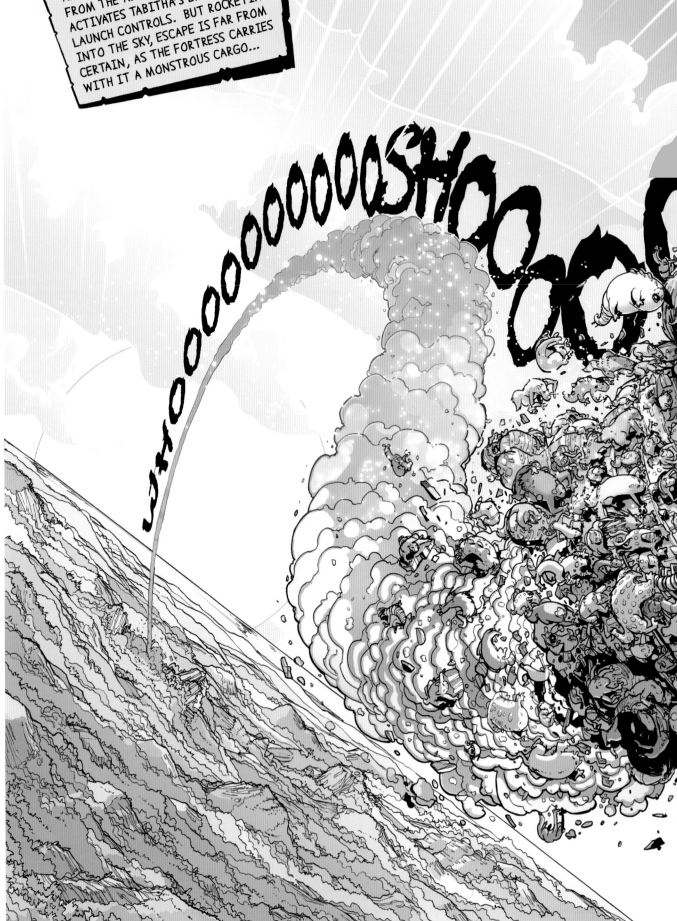

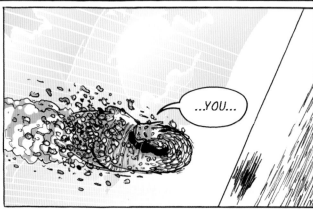

AT HOME WITH THE NUTS - #2
WHEN NOT FIGHTING CRIME, OUR INTREPID HEROES LIKE TO RELAX ONBOARD THEIR BASE, THE GALLEON DE MISTERIOS.